STEPHEN CLARKE and **RAB SHIELDS** are life coaches and weight-loss experts from Perth, Scotland, who are shaking up the health and wellness sphere with their informative and lighthearted videos on YouTube. They are also presenters of the BBC Scotland show *Secret Body*, piloted in 2019, and are currently filming the first season, for release in 2022.

www.thekiltedcoaches.com

THE KILTED COACHES
How to Stick to the Damn Plan

STEPHEN CLARKE and RAB SHIELDS

Luath Press Limited

EDINBURGH

www.luath.co.uk

First published 2021

ISBN: 978-1-910022-88-7

The authors' right to be identified as author of this book
under the Copyright, Designs and Patents Act 1988 has
been asserted.

The paper used in this book is recyclable. It is made
from low chlorine pulps produced in a low energy,
low emissions manner from renewable forests.

Printed and bound by
Grafo S.A., Bilbao

Typeset in 14 point Museo by
Main Point Books, Edinburgh

Text and images © Stephen Clarke and Rab Shields, 2021

To our families

Contents

INTRODUCTION

The birth of The Kilted Coaches

Having known one another from our paper-round days, fate would have it we'd find ourselves both becoming personal trainers and working from the same gym in Perth many years later. Our friendship naturally grew from there.

Through many whisky-fuelled chats we realised we shared the same view of the fitness industry:

that people were often following unsustainable training and eating regimes in a **quest to become healthy** – leading to an increase in stress, a decrease in results and mood, alongside far too many program relapses.

We spent over a decade preaching to our personal training clients about the

importance of happiness and

'allowing for life'.

But with our one-to-one business model and only so many hours in the day, our attempt to fix such a widespread issue was a drop in the ocean.

In another turn of fate, we became fathers around the same time.

We both wanted to maximise the **quality time** spent with our families, while still helping people to lose weight, make sustainable lifestyle changes and ultimately become happier within themselves.

We wanted to provide for our families and help even **MORE** people than before, in a **BIGGER** way. So we made the decision to take our principles and business model online and thus

'The Kilted Coaches' were born.

It's not always been plain sailing.

We've changed tactics and strategy a few times.

We've hit hurdles.

We've felt mentally and emotionally challenged.

We've even ground to a halt once or twice.

But one thing always remained.

Our vision.

We knew the health and fitness industry was missing something and we felt in our hearts that we could make a difference.

In essence,

we stuck to the damn plan.

1: Be yourself in HD

Many of you will have a vague idea of who you are. What you like, what you value in this world, what gets you out of bed in the morning and maybe even what gets you INTO bed... if you know what we mean. But 'vague' is about as defined as it gets for most folk.

Take some time to think about who **you** are, deep down. We mean **the real you**.

And more importantly,

who you want to be.

Because life is full of environments, people and experiences that will pull you away from your true identity.

When we first started making videos and shouting to the world about **health and happiness**, a friend gave us some advice which was so simple, but paved the way for who and what we are today.

That advice?

Be yourself... but
bigger.

And this is the same advice that we'd like to pass on to you.

Be a **bigger** version of you,

a **more colourful** version of you,

a **louder** version of you.

Be yourself in HIGH DEFINITION.

When we first had the idea of working together, we didn't call ourselves

The Kilted Coaches.

The full story would be outwith the scope of this book, but let's just say we were clean-cut, not a single hair on our chins... and our personalities were lost in the post.

All for the delusion of being more professional.

We still laugh to this day about that early incarnation of the business.

We simply were not being ourselves.

It wasn't until we put the kilt on, swore a few times and made our peace with the constant innuendos that we felt like we'd coloured ourselves in.

We'd become HD.

We have always enjoyed wearing kilts as the true Scotsmen that we are.

But in all honesty, we'd never worn them as much as we do now.

The kilt became our superhero costume.

There's an unspoken truth that when a Scotsman puts his kilt on, there's generally more **laughs**, and there's more **self-pride**, more **compassion** and more **connection** with others. The decision to make this part of our identity was a stroke of genius; now, every day we're 'working', we're overrun with all of the above.

Never underestimate the power of the clothes and accessories you wear. Are you dressing like the real you? What does your clothing say to your subconscious? What does your clothing say to others you are interacting with?

As soon as we decided we'd wear the kilts and become **The Kilted Coaches**, it seemed like we had 100% permission to be ourselves – but a bigger version! We'd come into our own just by understanding who we really were, exaggerating it a little bit, and then **singing to the world about our message of health and happiness and sticking to the damn plan.**

Here's how to express yourself in HD.

Too many people live their life not fully knowing who they are and settling for a mediocre expression of themselves. They find themselves reacting to situations in ways which are not true to who they really are. And afterwards, they might be a wee bit embarrassed and think, 'Oh, I should have stuck up for myself!' or 'I shouldn't have have blown the lid like that!'

The first step is to take some time to understand who, what and how you want to be.

Do you want to be resentful of the past or excited for the future?
Do you value your health?
Do you take pride in your relationships?
Do you honour honesty?

You also want to think about the things you eat, your level of activity, your lifestyle and daily habits.

A really good way of doing this is to imagine that somebody is telling your life story after you have departed this world. What you were like as a person, how you treated others, how you faced your fears

and how you stood up for what you felt was right.
Now hold that image **strong in your heart**
and portray it to the world.

Paint your true life's picture in your daily actions.

And as you live your authentic life, ask yourself:
Is this living my life in HD?

So, remember... take a wee bit of time to think about
who you are deep down as a person.

And more to the point, **who you want to be.**

Then let every thought, feeling and action be

unmistakably you.

2: What you want

Let's address the elephant in the room.

You've probably bought this book because you like Scotland and/or men in kilts.

It's full of big, colourful images, and it would be a great book for sitting on your coffee table to pick up and read now and again.

We've purposefully made the mindsets short for this very reason. But as you pick this book up and flick through the pages, we've filled it with little golden nuggets of inspiration, education and motivation that will help you improve your life and **stick to the damn plan**.

whatever yours may be.

We use the very same tactic throughout our website,

and across all our social media. We give you what you want and slip in what you need.

You can use this same tactic in your everyday life. Let's say you're on a weight loss journey and a friend of yours suggests meeting up for coffee and cake.

You might feel like the coffee is okay, but **you could do without the cake**.

Now, your friend might say they want to go for coffee and cake, but sometimes what they actually need is to talk, or to bond and share a connection with you.

So, give them, and yourself, WHAT YOU WANT.

Agree to coffee but rather than sitting in a café, **you could go for a nice walk instead.**

This means you won't have the cake and **you get a little exercise**.

Then, while you're walking, you can discuss how you're **losing weight** and that you **love** having their support.

Let's take another example. **You find yourself craving** sweet food like cake and chocolate. Ultimately, **you want a quick fix** for low energy and/ or mood.

This is an opportunity to give your body what it wants, while slipping in what it needs.

Sometimes some roast vegetables with a drizzle of oil and honey will give you that sweetness, but it will also give you lots of fibre and vitamins and minerals to give your body the sustenance that it needs.

Whenever you feel yourself wanting anything ask yourself

'What do I really NEED at this moment?'

3: The ultimate Scottish workout

'Who needs a gym when you've got Scotland?'

We coined this phrase very early on in our Kilted Coaches journey, initially as a proud advertisement for Scotland, but latterly for educational reasons. We made a video for social media with this very title and although it contained a little tongue-in-cheek humour, the underlying message was there.

We both trained up within a gym environment, surrounded by the sweat and hustle of like-minded fitness-seekers, all of us working around one another in our own quest for physical perfection. Even typing that makes us cringe now!

Some gym-goers are drawn to specialised methods of training such as powerlifting or bodybuilding, but for the majority, the goal is to get **fitter**, **healthier** and possibly
lose some body fat.

Gyms come in all shapes and sizes, and to fit all budgets for those people that are willing to 'rent' equipment on a monthly basis to work towards their goals. What all gyms have in common is, quite simply, varying degrees of 'heavy stuff' coupled with some 'stuff to help you move'.

And the more you're willing to pay, the more variety you'll have of both sets of equipment.

Back when we were both personal trainers, it was always an interesting and unique challenge, when delivering a home training session, to adjust the workout based on the ability of the client and the environment. Decisions had to be made on the basis of how fit the person was and what equipment and space they had in their home.

Personal training in a gym is easy. You are spoiled for choice and your only issue is how busy the gym is at the time you are training your client. The busier it is, the less likely they'll be able to use every piece of equipment you want them to.

But home training always challenged the old noggin, forcing us both to **adapt** and **think on our feet**, making use of furniture, doorways, flat walls and, in some cases, garden equipment. The goal was

always to give the client **the best workout possible** to progress them towards their goals. You had to ensure you could achieve that, no matter where your planned exercise session took place, whether at a gym or in their own home.

What we learned from the experience of home training was that you really don't need a lot of fancy equipment to get a good workout in. We can work the muscles really hard by simply using the tools around us. Sometimes that means looking at objects and ornaments with a 'fitter' set of eyes.

'And if you're afraid to get your hands dirty...
Stick to dumbbells.'

Let's face it, we have all become a little precious when it comes to dirt and mud these days. Our skin is such a fantastic layer of armour around our bodies. It's soft, yet firm, with low permeability coupled with a fantastic 'repair or replace' capacity, and best of all... it's easy to clean!

And yet if we were to ask you to pick up a dirty rock or log a few times in order to improve your health, there's a high chance you'll check said rock for traces of detritus and base your decision on how soiled the rock is to begin with.

There are so many people out there who are too intimidated by the gym environment, people who also don't feel they have enough room to exercise in their own home. Yet they all have a membership to the only gym they truly ever need:

the outdoors!

Want to do some cardio?
Great, go for a walk!

Want to do some intense cardio?
Go for a run or climb a hill.

Want to firm up those muscles?
Lift some rocks.

Want to feel more dynamic and energetic?
Jump some logs or bound through the heather.

All the equipment is there if you are willing to spend a little time thinking about how to adapt it to what you want to achieve and how to utilise it in a safe manner.

Now of course we speak from a very 'Scottish privileged' position here and we understand that not everybody has hills and countryside on their

doorstep. But ask yourself this: how far would you be willing to travel to get to your gym? Some people drive all the way across town to get their workouts done.

If **your gym is the outdoors** and your nearest wood is a 20-minute cycle or drive or bus-ride away, there's no reason why you shouldn't make that journey to better yourself.

You might say that the weather would be a potential barrier. That your warm and cosy gym has shelter.

Yes, this is true, but **there's no such thing as 'bad weather', just poor clothing choices**, so dress accordingly.

Besides, working outdoors gives you access to an abundant source of the most vital nutrient:

oxygen.

The one thing we simply can't live without.

Exercising indoors, especially if the ventilation is not of the highest quality, means a lot of the time you are breathing in recycled air.

When training outdoors, you don't have this problem. Unless, of course, you are next to a busy road and you have other pollutants to concern yourself with.

But let's just assume you are as lucky as we are here in Scotland and have access to green areas where fresh oxygen is being produced through photosynthesis.

That old saying, 'Feeling unwell? **Go out and get some fresh air**' truly does have merit.

'So,' you might ask, 'what does this all mean in terms of **sticking to the damn plan**?'

Well, it's quite simple.

Squash any barriers regarding lack of a gym or fear of a gym and just

get outdoors to train!

Nature has given you plenty of tools to work your muscles if a gym is not for you.

And always remember, regardless of where you are in your personal fitness journey, it really doesn't matter if your workouts are social media worthy or tagged in at fancy gyms, as long as you're making progress, whether you're starting again after a long lay-off, or starting from scratch.

Wherever you begin, as long as you're making positive steps forward, then your workout is worthy.

Think about where you are right now and make the first logical step. That's all that matters.

Don't let any gym barriers hold you back.

4: Get out of your own way

Let's face it, we all have more than one side to us.

We have our motivated side, driven and goal-oriented and typically taking care of our work tasks. We have our loving and caring side that we wear when we want to show affection to the ones we love. We have our dreamer side that forward-plans for us, sometimes creating almost impossible, but desirable, goals. And, of course, we all have our negative side; the part that doesn't believe you will succeed and will remind you about it at any given moment.

Now, if you let that negative facet rule the roost, you would be a pretty miserable individual. Your dreams would feel unattainable, your productivity would feel diminished and your ability to love and care for those around you would be muted.

So, it would be fair to say that for optimal results (in life) we would want to minimise the amount of time that part of us is in control.

Sometimes we don't even know who is at the helm. And why would we? Thinking too much about it causes 'analysis paralysis'.

However, the question to ask is:
Are you creating or are you reacting?

We're always creating our own lives, whether that be physically or mentally. But more often than not, you can find yourself reacting to your environment.

Let's take something as simple as this. When you start the day, are you reacting to your emails and notifications, or are you planning and creating opportunities for the day?

When you spend too much time reacting, your brain gets into a heightened state of panic and the negative side of you becomes more prominent. You might find yourself using phrases like 'bad things come in threes...'

Really? Why?

That saying alone invites another two negative situations after you've dealt with the first. Yet we continue to do it. At times we wear our 'firefighting' skills like a badge of honour, because life has taught us it's going to throw stuff in our direction and we congratulate ourselves for making it through. Crikey, Elton John even sang a song about that!

You might still be standing, but are you creating? Or are you still reacting? There's a rewrite of those lyrics for you.

When we are constantly reacting to our environment, we tend to overthink things. We attempt to pre-empt disasters before they happen. This is the basis of anxiety. And reacting and overthinking get in the way of progress.

So, how do you get out of your own way?

Our minds work on both conscious and subconscious levels, the former being our daily decision-making pilot, and the latter our smarter, hardworking employee that works away in the background and achieves more than our conscious mind will ever know.

Our conscious mind is easily distracted and most affected by emotions in the short term. As the pilot of our ship, it encounters many problems that our subconscious mind is equipped to solve through lateral thinking. The issue here is that we tend to identify with the conscious mind, and resist allowing

the subconscious co-pilot to take the helm. Our subconscious mind will be fired up to work out a solution, but our conscious mind just says, 'Fuck that.'

Basically, to get out of your own way, **you must let your subconscious mind do its job and problem-solve for you.** Don't let your conscious mind become a self-destructive force.

We've all done it. You're working towards a plan of good health, you've been training hard, but you've had a long day at work and you're tired. Maybe you were supposed to be exercising that evening. And then your conscious mind starts to make stupid decisions that your subconscious mind would kick its ass for like: 'Oh, you've had a long day and are a bit too tired to train.' Your emotions take over and you allow yourself to be convinced that it's okay not to train because you're tired. Poor you.

We often think we know what's best for us, our pilot airing a sense of superiority while the subconscious advises gently, 'Are you sure you want to do this? You'll regret it tomorrow.' Sure enough, we wake the next day and wish we had trained the night before. We feel flat because we have neglected our goal. We feel like we have failed.
We got in our own way.

When you set goals, you are telling both parts of your mind that this is important to you.

Place value in what it is you are trying to achieve.

Set out a plan of action.

While we are aware of what our pilot is doing, our subconscious mind is beavering away in the background on hundreds of smaller tasks that all help towards that goal.

So, **in order to stick to the damn plan**, it's important that your conscious mind does exactly that – and does not waver with emotion, or let itself be swayed by comfort. If it was important to you when you set the goal, it should always be important to you.

Get out of your own way and

stick to the damn plan!

5: Grow forwards, measure backwards

Measuring backwards? Are you insane?

The analogy we like to use here is that you're climbing, let's say, Ben Nevis, the highest Munro in Scotland. **Definitely worth conquering.**

Picture yourself, walking boots on, rucksack on your back, climbing upwards to the top. It's steep and the terrain can be precarious, so you are focusing on each small step. And you're knackered, because you've got your lunch in your rucksack. If you're anything like us, you'll want to enjoy a good banquet at the top of a Munro to celebrate bagging it. After an hour or so, your legs begin to burn, your breathing becomes laboured and you start to question your ability to make it to the top.

While it's good to set a goal, the only real place that progress exists is in the past. Or in the case of the hill climb, behind you. Looking back and realising the progress you've made gives you the extra energy you need to **carry on to the summit**. So, when you're on any sort of journey, whether it's climbing a mountain, or building your personal fitness, or achieving weight-loss, it's always important to

set goals.

Rather than delving into the depths of goal-setting, let's keep it simple.

Step 1: What is it you want to achieve and why is it important to you?

Step 2: When would you like to achieve it by? (long-term goal)

Step 3: What would be a good first milestone on your journey towards this goal? (medium-term goal)

Step 4: What daily habits would you need to incorporate into your life to achieve this goal? (short-term goals)

Step 5: Start

As soon as you start this journey, you will begin to make progress.

But how will you know?

Going back to the Ben Nevis analogy, every now and again you've got to turn around and enjoy the view. Look at where you've come from, look at the progress you've already made and that will be your motivation to continue. Without comparing your current location to your starting position, you can never track your progress.

You might 'feel' like you've had success, but without a tangible set of results you will be relying on your intuition alone. This has its benefits from time to time, but for solid progress you need solid data, and the numbers won't lie.

Whatever journey you are on, every now and then STOP, turn around and look at how far you've come.

The motivation gained from this practice will drive you on towards your goal.

Grow forwards

and

measure backwards.

6: Relationship counselling... with yourself

We all have that little voice in our heads.

Most of the time it's an incessant but harmless running commentary. 'I'm too hot, I'm going to open that window.' 'That's a nice jacket.' 'Oh good, it's lunchtime.' 'I wonder what they look like naked', and so on... and on and on.

You might even be thinking right now, 'I don't have a voice inside my head.' But there you go, the voice inside your head just told you that you don't have a voice inside your head.

Of course, this is completely normal, but you would do well to start listening a little more intently, as this running commentary voice can quickly turn from negative, paranoid and fearful, to confident, hopeful and excited, and then back to pessimistic.

Let's say you want to lose some weight and you've set a target of losing 10lbs over the next four weeks.

Does that voice say things like, 'I can do this easily, no problem at all. I can't wait to fit back into my jeans'? Or is it saying things like, 'I've tried this before and I just can't lose more than a few pounds. I enjoy my wine too much to make this weight loss anything close to sustainable'?

Now imagine that voice in your head was a real person that you just met.

Based on what they are saying to you, would you invite them out for coffee and a chat?

Would you invite them to meet your friends or play with your kids?

Or would you tell them to fuck off?

The relationship you have with that voice in your head is probably the most important relationship you never knew you had.

And remember,

all relationships need work.

Our tip is, journal it all.

It's hard to make sense of anything while it's still rattling around in your head, so get into the habit of writing it all down, especially when you feel yourself being negative.

Get yourself a nice journal or even just take notes on your phone. As you see the words written down, you can start to pull them apart and shine some logic onto them. Where did that mindset come from? Was this something you were told by your parents? Were you bullied as a kid, and has this made you doubt yourself now? Were you always the shy kid and never fully believed in yourself? Maybe you're the loud one, but confidence is just a mask for your insecurities. **Dissect that negative voice and expose it for what it is.**

Continue putting that voice under the microscope and you'll find that those negative words will start to lose all meaning. Each time they pop into your head they won't have as much impact since you'll already know where they came from and that it's generally bullshit. In time the voice will change to be **more positive** and **uplifting** as you develop a healthy, supportive and vibrant relationship with yourself.

7: Put down the shovel!

When you go to the beach, you've got to dig a hole, right? You simply have to. It's like the law. And if it's not, it should be.

If you are anything like us, you will dig as deep as you can possibly go until you get tired, or until common sense kicks in and you realise how dangerous it is leaving a big gaping hole in the middle of a public beach. At that point, you will fill it back in (after taking a proud photo for social media of course) and sit back, feeling accomplished.

You dug that hole and it was epic!

We are going to rewind time slightly here and tell you all about two sandpits close to where we grew up. They sat side by side, one shallower than the other. As young lads we knew which sandpit to use – the one we could get in and out of easily enough, no panic and no drama.

Then there was the other pit... the **deeper** pit, which is interesting, as it actually had less sand in it. If you climbed in there, it was a real struggle to get out. With the granite stone sides there was nowhere to grip and the sand only added to the lack of friction. The diameter wasn't huge, either, so you couldn't get much of a run at it.

It wasn't impossible for our young selves to escape from, just really difficult, and we are sure many a child was stuck in there, screaming for help, on lots of occasions.

In life, we sometimes feel like we are in a hole with no obvious means to escape. Occasionally this hole is one we dig for ourselves, which only adds salt to the wound (see what we did there). And sometimes the more we struggle, the deeper we dig, until getting out might seem impossible.

But here's the thing.

If you want to get yourself out of the hole, you must first put down the shovel.

With regards to health and fitness, or life in general, you can dig yourself a hole by eating badly, skipping exercise and making choices that you **KNOW** are detrimental to what you want to achieve.

You might sit up late at night wishing you looked and felt a certain way, while sipping a glass of wine and shovelling dip-laden crisps into your mouth for comfort.

You might sit up late at night and feel like you are in a deep hole of unhealthiness.

The only way to get out of the hole is to stop making it worse – to begin with. That's why we're asking you to throw down the shovel.

If you want to get **fit and healthy**, but you're still eating rubbish, you must first stop eating rubbish, because that is making things worse.

What you have to understand is that we humans are very habitual creatures and we do things in **cycles**.

You may be in the cycle of trying crash diets or eating rubbish food; or it could even be something that you think is a positive thing that always ends in a negative, such as restricting your calorie intake

too much, which in turn reduces your metabolism, leading you to fall off the wagon.

You wake up the next day and you've put all the weight back on again, plus some! It's a cycle, and you're digging yourself a deeper and deeper hole.

Put down the fucking shovel.

So, if you want to stick to the damn plan and making a change is high on your list of priorities, then have a look at the self-destructive things you are doing in your life and stop doing them!

Put down the shovel!

8: Value your time

Time.

It's the only real currency you have in your life.

Time is a perishable commodity and as much as we can use terms like 'make time', 'save time' and 'buy time' none of these statements is actually true.

Yet our time is valuable and we can all agree that 'wasting time' is a feeling no one enjoys.

(Let's hope this next part doesn't depress you too much.)

There are 24 hours in a day (or 1,440 minutes, if you'd prefer to make it seem bigger). If you have good sleeping habits, we estimate you will be unconscious for a third of that.

16 hours remain (960 minutes for the optimists).

Let's assume the average person works for 8 hours, plus 30 minutes travelling either side.

7 hours remain (420 minutes).

You then spend around an hour a day practising self-care (washing, brushing teeth, preparing meals) and another hour consuming your meals throughout the day.

5 hours remain (300 minutes).

Then let's assume you are a motivated individual that spends at least an hour a day on their health, so either a workout or even a dog walk.

4 hours remain (240 minutes).

Lastly, let's scalp 2 hours for family care (if you live in a busy household). This would include caring for, cleaning for and just generally giving your time away to commitments you may have.

2 hours remain (120 minutes or 7,200 seconds if you like).

That time is YOURS! And this is only a rough estimate, as some people feel they have even less.

So 7,200 seconds belong to you each day to do as you see fit. But before you know it, you

haemorrhage these vital seconds waiting.

Yes, WAITING!

Have you ever stopped to consider just how much time you spend waiting. You wait for transport, you wait in queues, you wait for lights to turn green, you wait for lifts to reach your floor, you wait for replies in messaging apps, with that infamous typing symbol keeping our eyes glued to a conversation. You wait for files to upload and websites to download, you even wait for the kettle to boil.

It really is incredible. To be fair, we as humans are a fairly patient species. A lot of our waiting time is endured out of politeness. It might be waiting on a friend popping round or waiting on a scheduled business meeting to begin. But at what point do you cross over from being polite to not valuing your time?

A few years back we had an experience with a major TV channel here in the UK.

The production company got in contact and wanted us to come on their show, and we said yes. We blocked a week off our businesses to do this filming.

(Please note there was no money involved in this TV project.)

The production company came back to us and said, 'Actually, there's an extra two days required to film sections about your backstory.'

So, we said, 'All right, let's make that happen.'

We added another two days on top (which involved cancelling a shopping trip that had already been organised). And we then received an email asking us to change the dates.

We played ball and made the adjustments, rescheduling clients to make it work.

The second of the backstory days, we had to arrange to have ten people available (family and friends), as part of the filming, the idea being that we'd to cook for our guests to let the audience get more of an insight into who we were. As we are both family men with young children, this meant we had to organise alternative childcare, not just for our own children, but also for our guests.

Then this production company emailed once again to reschedule. There was no 'Can you?' or

'Is it possible to?' They said, 'We are changing your backstory filming to this date.'

We'd had enough.

When we calculated it, that one decision to reschedule affected 55 people just on our end, between childcare, our guests, our guests' childcare, rescheduled clients and their dependants too.

So we pulled the plug.

In doing so, we had made not just a stand, but a statement. This production company had zero regard for our time or the time of our guests. They valued their own interests above ours. Okay, more power to them.

But we took that power back when we told them NO. We reminded ourselves that our time is valuable and when people don't appreciate your time, they don't deserve it.

For your own personal development, you have to use that same level of discretion. You choose the boundaries/thresholds of what is acceptable and what's taking the piss.

We watched an Al Pacino movie once where the character he played stated that he didn't wait longer than ten minutes in a meeting before leaving: 'Ten minutes allows for traffic, anything else is just disrespectful,' he said, and we have to agree with him.

You have to establish your own boundaries and be sure to enforce them.

As you know, we are big believers in sticking to the damn plan! Whatever the plan may be, you set the plan and you stick to that damn plan. When those around you are constantly changing the plan or running late (and not sticking to it), what they are not saying out loud, but showing with their actions, is 'my time is more important than yours'.

When we interact with those around us, whether family, friends or business associates, we are teaching those people how they should treat us. Yes, the way people treat YOU is based on how you allow yourself to be treated. You might not be aware you're doing that, but you are. It's a constantly fluid discussion.

As we said above, it's important to set your own thresholds and decide what you feel is acceptable and in line with your values. But, once set, you have to enforce those values because, if you don't, others will value their time over yours.

This lesson is really about respecting your own time, and respecting other people's time. We've all got our priorities and life will absolutely get in the way. Sometimes friends will genuinely need to reschedule, as will you yourself, here and there. But there are only 24 hours in a day and no matter how rich you are, you cannot get more than that.

You cannot buy your time back.

You'll never get your time back.

So, choose how you spend your time very, very wisely. Respect your own time, but respect other people's time as well.

Value your time and stick to the damn plan!

9: Don't let your flaws define you

So often in life we add weight to negative thoughts and opinions, especially when they are directed at oneself. They say for every one bad comment it takes ten compliments to balance it, and this holds true with any imperfections we perceive in ourselves. When we look in the mirror, our eyes are drawn to areas we are not happy with – to scars, blemishes, perceived imperfections.

We naturally focus on our flaws, or the things we don't have. Like a ripped set of abs to press through a shirt, a firm bottom that would look great in any tight jeans, a body that would make any bikini look great.

We turn our attention on what we don't have or what is missing when compared to our heroes or our social media icons. Some might say this can be useful and that, as an ever-progressing species, we try our best to improve our lives in any way we can. But for others, focusing on their flaws can swiftly become a slippery slope into the abyss of unhappiness.

So, focus on what you do have
and not what you don't have.

Growing up, we absolutely loved dinosaurs! Blockbuster Hollywood movies shone a spotlight on some of the largest and fiercest of beasts, with the Tyrannosaurus Rex being the most iconic of them all.

When someone says, 'Name a vegetable,' most people think of a carrot. If you're asked to think of a dinosaur, you'll likely picture a T-Rex!

Seventeen feet tall, 40 feet from nose to tail and weighing in at around 8 metric tonnes, this monstrous predator stalked the Earth, terrorising its vegetarian counterparts with a gargantuan bite that could deliver a crushing force of around 60 thousand Newtons (according to some smart science guys). We all know what it looks like, its massive thighs supporting a powerful frame, headed off with those famous jaws, with two little clawed paws tucked underneath.

Now if a T-Rex judged itself on its boxing ability, its personal best at press-ups or its juggling skills, it'd

probably be pretty miserable. Historic king of the jungle or not, if a T-Rex had feelings, we're sure if it spent too long gazing into a crystal clear lake and focusing on those tiny little paws, it would feel insecure.

But the T-Rex doesn't give a Jurassic fuck.
(Yes, we know the T-Rex lived in the Cretaceous period but that wouldn't fit the joke.)

The T-Rex has thick, thunderous legs for running and the biggest jaws ever. It stalks with confidence, it hunts with pride. Small paws mean nothing against gigantic razor-sharp teeth and a bite worse than its bark!

There's something called the negativity bias (also known as the negativity effect), which states that when things are equal in intensity, those of a more negative nature have a greater effect on our thoughts.

Basically, as our thoughts skim over anything, we tend to dwell on the negative and this attention adds weight to its validity. This pattern will make you feel unhappy.

When trying to make changes to your health and fitness, this negativity bias might lead you to look

for reasons that you can't do something, adding substance to the excuse and then justifying your reasons for either not starting, or quitting early.

'I have bad knees so can't exercise.'
'I'm too old to get fit now.'
'I don't know what I'm doing.'

These are just some of the barriers we place in our way, a list of the things we CAN'T do when in fact the solutions are always more straightforward.

Bad knees? Okay, what **CAN** you do that doesn't involve the knees?

Too old to get fit? **You're never too old.** Just start slowly and take it easy. Listen to your body. Focus on what feels right and build from there.

Don't know what you're doing? That's okay, **find a coach and get the answers**.

When we make a conscious effort to

focus on the positives and overcome negativity

adjusting our mindset from 'CAN'T' to 'CAN' will make all the difference to your success.

Always play to your strengths.

If you're on a fitness or weight-loss journey, think about the things that you're already good at and get even better at them.

Do the best you can with your weaknesses.

Set small achievable goals around them and make your peace with the fact that these 'weak' areas are not your best, but they **WILL** get better in time, no matter how long that takes.

So, in order to stick to the damn plan, make sure you identify your strengths and **work harder** at them, reassured by knowing that any weaknesses will improve in time.

10: Dump your irrational fears

We all experience fear from time to time. The question is what do you do when you feel that fear creeping into your heart? Or maybe you have plans for your life, but you're left in no man's land, struggling to move forward because of what 'might' happen.

Fuck that!

First of all, it's important to establish the difference between fear and danger. They are two very different things.

Fear is nothing more than an emotional response to danger, perceived or actual.

Fear is helpful in extreme situations when you don't have time to formulate a logical response. Let's say you're out hiking and a bear charges at you. Fear will create a reaction of fight, flight or freeze. You'll try to fight the bear (not advised), or you'll run away, or you'll do nothing and hope the bear leaves you alone.

Fear is not real. Danger is real.

You can have a fear of heights, for instance. Now the danger may exist – falling from a great height will hurt and, if high enough, could even kill you. However, the fear is only in your head. Ask yourself, is this fear helping me or hindering me? Is it better to have a fear of heights or just be very aware of the dangers and act accordingly?

Say there was a job promotion, but you didn't go for it for fear of failing. Or for fear of other people in the office seeing you were trying to go for it and not achieving it. Fear of embarrassment perhaps. Fear can prevent us from taking action and if you always give in to it you'll soon find your life hasn't moved forward and your dreams have left you behind.

Rationalise everything.

In many everyday situations you'll have more than enough time to create a response to any danger. This is completely different to fear. But this is not the real problem facing most people when it comes to sticking to the damn plan.

Fear, it would seem, can disable even the most inspired ambitions through nothing more than illusion.

If you have a plan for your life, a grand vision, but you're a little scared of embarrassment, regret or some other imaginary outcome just ask yourself – is this a rational fear?

Sometimes this thought exercise is enough to dump your irrational fears, but other times we need more.

Sometimes logic doesn't stand a chance against fear.

Okay, yes, we get it! Sometimes you don't want to hear all that logical stuff and you just feel fucking scared.

What do you do when you've got this inherent fear of going to the gym, weighing yourself, having that awkward conversation, confrontation, sticking up for yourself, sticking to the damn plan?

Courage!
That's what.
Motherfucking courage.

You never get over fear. You also can't go under it, around it and you certainly don't want to just turn away from it.

You find the courage within you. Approach that fear and go through it.

Sticking to the damn plan sometimes means getting uncomfortable. But, as your comfort zone is made up of the things you do on a regular basis, when you smash through your fears, guess what? You just added that very thing to your comfort list. Or at least made it easier to tackle the next time it comes up.

Anyone who has ever experienced fear will also tell you that all they want is courage. You've most likely been there yourself at some point in your life and you might even be there now.

The only way to ever express courage is if you feel the fear first. Courage literally cannot exist without fear.

But once you're done with this little dance of fear and courage for a while and you've made your peace with the reality that they not only co-exist but are both essential if you are going to get anywhere with your plan,

that's when
your confidence
will start to emerge.

Confidence in knowing that when the next dose of fear hits you, you can be

sure as hell
you'll find the courage

once again to **move through it**.

11: Fuck your excuses

Oh, so you have excuses for not sticking to the damn plan?

As you read this book, take your time with every sentence of every paragraph in every chapter. Hunt high and low, get a second opinion if you wish. You can even read between the lines. The challenge is to find at least one fuck we give about your excuses but in the end... you'll come up short.

That may seem harsh but it's meant with love.

Let us explain...

'Current You' is here, right now, reading this book with ambitions for your health and fitness, your career, maybe even for your love life. 'Future You' has a big smile on your face, proud of your achievements.

'Future You' is grateful. Grateful, not just for your successes, but for the character you've built along the way. The **resilience**, the **confidence**, the

determination, the **compassion** and **understanding** for yourself and the **willpower** you've cultivated.

Now in between 'Current You' and 'Future You' are obstacles of all shapes and sizes.

Some of them you'll see as nothing more than a hurdle to get over, others will appear as brick walls you just can't get through. When you come across these obstacles, you're going to do one of two things.

You're either going to **tackle it** and **overcome it** or you're going to shy away from it.

Now, every time you shy away from an obstacle it transforms, right before your eyes, into an excuse. Each time this happens, 'Future You' gets farther and farther away. If you continue this pattern, all of your obstacles will eventually turn into excuses, and 'Future You' will disappear completely. Rather than having a 'Current You' and a 'Future You', all that's going to be left is you and your excuses.

So we say: fuck your excuses!

Don't get us wrong, we both know what it's like to fall prey to this mindset without even realising it.

From experience, we know that the trick is to be mindful of 'Future You' as much as possible and conscious of anything that pulls you away from that.

When you turn an obstacle into an excuse, it's your way of saving your ego. It takes a lot of energy and determination to get over these hurdles, so it's tempting to take the path of least resistance. Then, to make you feel better about not achieving your dream future, your ego prefers to put the blame on someone/something else. And you blame the excuse.

Can't lose weight because of genetics, a medical condition, or even 'that's just the way I am'.
Can't be financially secure because I need money to make money.
Can't find love because all the good ones are taken, I have issues with intimacy, my town is too small.
Can't be happy because I've experienced trauma, I suffer with depression, I'm stuck.

Life is tough sometimes. You may not be to blame for your hurdles and barriers, the trauma you experienced or the start to life that was less than ideal.

But **you are 100 per cent responsible** for dealing with it all now. Nobody else is going to do it for you.

Now we understand that the points we're making here may sound a little harsh and the last thing we want is for anyone to be upset. So, for the sake of clarity, we'll just say a few things before we go on. We're very aware that working through things like PTSD, chronic anxiety, depression and a whole host of other conditions can feel debilitating. The last thing you want to hear is Fuck Your Excuses. But the truth of the matter is, there are people healing from these conditions every day and although it's tough, we know you can do it too. It just takes time. If you're ever in doubt, ask yourself this question: What's more helpful... to believe that things are hopeless, or to believe that, although its tough, you can get through anything?

When you boil it all down, **the only thing in your way, the only thing that stops you in your tracks, is you.** Nobody likes failing or feeling like they might fail, and the easiest way to not fail is to not try. If you don't try, it's impossible to fail, right?

So, rather than facing your fears, making big decisions, having that awkward conversation, be willing to go to the land of discomfort and stay there for a while or processing your trauma fully, it's easier to turn these things into excuses. This way your ego is saved. Your life is still 'as good as it can be' within your self-imposed limitations. The real hilarity begins when you start justifying things to your friends, family, colleagues and even to complete strangers.

I've tried losing weight, but...
I'd love to be happy, but unfortunately...
In an ideal world I'd have found love by now, but...

People will always be polite, they'll sympathise, they'll agree with you. But the truth is you say these things for YOUR benefit, not theirs. Your friends, family, colleagues and even those complete strangers would much rather hear how you came across an obstacle and overcame it. How you reached to the depths of your soul and found the drive to push on. How you made the scary decision to stop settling for second best. How you became sick and tired of being sick and tired. How you put your ego to one side, admitted you didn't know what you were doing and asked for help.

We hope you have read this chapter in the light it was intended and that at the very least you're looking at your plan with **fresh eyes**, **renewed motivation** and **a smile on your face**, knowing 'Future You' has **overcome a bunch of shit** and is
ready for more.

12: Get comfortable being uncomfortable

Regardless of the specifics of your own personal plan for your life, I think we can all agree on one thing. If you're reading this book, you have an

aspiration

beyond what you are currently experiencing. Probably something involving

health, happiness

and

success.

It's fair to say that if you want to experience something different, then you have to make changes.

Your body is an energy saving machine. We are constantly adapting to our environment, physically, mentally and emotionally, so that when you repeatedly experience the same thing, you use less energy each time. We see this play out in the gym when you lift weights or start jogging. At first your body expends a lot of energy as it experiences something new. It's not just the exercise itself that requires energy but the adaptation afterwards.

Beginners' weight-loss efforts are usually successful in the short term. But as you start to adapt to your routine, the muscles become stronger and more efficient, so the same workout doesn't require as much energy and there is no adaptation required afterwards. This is when you find your **comfort zone** and you may experience a plateau in your results.

This is not just applicable to your fitness. Your whole body and brain use the same system of stimulus in the form of stress followed by adaptation.

However, **too much stress can be counterproductive**. Stress can overwhelm you, leading to a lack of

recovery, with less willingness to experience stress subsequently.

Your growth and personal development sit in the sweet spot just outside your comfort zone. The place where you experience that heightened sense of vulnerability; the place where you can't help but focus more.

Being uncomfortable is where your true power is.

When you're uncomfortable, you will take massive leaps forward. When you're uncomfortable, you will stick to the damn plan.

Of course, doing this once is not enough. It must be done constantly for you to continue the journey and see your vision become reality. So, get comfortable being uncomfortable.

13: New surroundings bring new thoughts

'Go somewhere new.'
'Try something different.'

I'm sure you've heard these sayings at some point in your life. Perhaps you've disregarded them as clichés and carried on with your day. Or perhaps you've said to yourself, 'I wish I had the time to do that,' and disregarded them anyway.

We always find it interesting how much people will drive themselves into the ground during a heavy working period with the promise of a holiday at the end of it. Sometimes they will work long, ridiculous hours to get assignments completed, even bringing their work home with them.

Then, when they go on holiday and relax, stress levels reduce, their minds clear and they solve problems they had been stuck on for months in the office. They come back from their trip rejuvenated and are far more productive in the workplace.

Time passes and they begin driving themselves into the ground once more and the cycle repeats.

The interesting part is that they view the holiday as a way of **recharging the body**, a way of giving it a rest to come back ready to hit it hard again. What a lot of people don't realise is just how beneficial being somewhere new and different is to our problem-solving abilities.

You have probably marvelled at the way a child's mind is like a sponge. We take our children new places to experience new sights, smells, textures – and adventures. Children love it because they are always learning, growing and developing.

As adults we are really no different. But we are prone to thinking we know everything, and for this reason no longer invite new stimuli into our lives as much as we probably should.

Albert Einstein once said: **'We can't solve problems by using the same kind of thinking we used when we created them.'** He was right.

And the best way to find a **new mindset** is to change your surroundings. To put it simply, go somewhere new!

That doesn't necessarily mean jetting off anywhere fancy. It can be visiting a new park, walking along a beach you've never been to before or exploring a forest you've only just found. By going somewhere new, you will be giving your brain a fresh stimulus, getting it all fired up and working as it should. Seeing things you don't take for granted or fully understand challenges the mind to problem-solve afresh. And wherever you go, be sure to leave any worries behind. **This sometimes means popping your phone onto no-data mode** so that you can't receive anything that will ruin your experience.

Another benefit of going somewhere new is getting out of the monotonous rut we sometimes find ourselves in, repeating tasks day after day, getting the feeling that our future is entirely predictable. You wake up in the same bed, then go through the same morning routine. Make coffee, have breakfast, go to work, come home, have your dinner, watch TV, then go back to bed. And for anyone who looks after a small child, add 'make meal for child, clean up meal, clean up mess on floor, wash child, tidy up toys, put washing on, make child snack, clean up after snack, tidy up toys again, make child's dinner, clean up dinner, clean up child...' You get the idea.

It's important to establish that **as humans, we are NOT machines** and therefore performing the same tasks over and over again won't really damage our equipment as such (we self-heal/repair) but our software will eventually malfunction, without a doubt! Or put simply... our minds will break down and our happiness will suffer.

One of the **key messages** we have always promoted throughout our journey as The Kilted Coaches is to shout about

the balance
of health and happiness.

The choices we make on our quest to be healthy should always be making us happy at the same time (with the exception of burpees).

So, when sticking to the damn plan, be sure to give your mind exercise, as well as your muscles. You might just find yourself creating a new vision for your future. At the very least, your stress levels will be reduced – and we're sure everyone could benefit from that in this busy world of today.

14: Cheating the system

Cheating the system? Yup, sometimes sticking to the damn plan means we have to cheat the damn system.

Take your fitness, health and nutrition for example. Let's say it's January and you want to make some changes. You might say something like, 'That's it, I'm going to make big changes this month. I'm going to commit to training five days per week, I'm going to eat salads and not eat takeaways or chocolate and I'm going to have an awesome mindset.' No doubt, like everyone else, you will start off with the best of intentions. But then inevitably you begin to struggle and find it difficult to maintain what you've set out to do, because you've been so absolute with your intentions. You may have planned five days per week for your training sessions, given set dates, possibly even set specific times – every morning, 7 o'clock!

You must always remember that when you start to succeed, certain parts of your brain and body adapt to this new routine, which makes future success more likely. But the opposite is also true. When you fail at something, you make further failure more likely. This is why so many people say things like 'I just don't have any willpower'.

Willpower is not the issue!

The issue is what you have set out in front of you.

When you don't succeed in your unrealistic plans, it's seen (from your subconscious point of view) as failure. Failure precipitates more failure.

Every day you stick to the damn plan you make it easier to continue to do so. So, let's be clever about what we define as 'the plan'.

Is the plan training five days per week, or is the plan to improve your fitness consistently and to maintain your health and happiness for the rest of your life?

Is the plan to never have takeaways, or to have them sporadically enough to allow your health to improve?

Is the plan to cut out chocolate completely, or to cut it out enough so that when you do have it you really fucking enjoy it?

Don't ever be afraid to modify your exercise routine to fix the needs of the week. It's about training 100 per cent when you feel 100 per cent. And if you're not feeling 100 per cent, then just do what you can. You're still doing a workout and therefore still sticking to the damn plan.

Let's say you've been up through the night with the family, or your kids have kept you awake, and the next day you feel like you can't do your full workout. Take a few seconds and ask yourself what CAN you do? Three quarters of it? Half of it? Maybe just a warm-up and stretch? You don't have to commit to doing the whole thing. Then, when you're feeling fresh again, you can get straight back to your full workouts.

Factoring in an

'adapt when needed' protocol

to your plan, as long as it's an honest and mindful adaptation, can be **one of the best things you can do for your success.**

Let's consider another trap you might fall into and how we can cheat the system. If you schedule in three hours per week for your training, whether that be pilates, weight training, running or yoga, and all of a sudden, you don't have the time or the energy to commit to that three hours, inevitably you'll drop sessions. The subconscious will notice that you've dropped a session and because you've made it okay to drop one session, then you're more likely to drop another one, and then another one. This can start to snowball very fast. Before you realise it, you've gone six months and rather than being left with awesome results you're left with nothing but your excuses. 'I've been too busy.' 'I don't have enough time.' 'Oh, I'm too tired, because the kids are keeping me up.'

What we're saying is,

cheat the system.

Don't skip sessions! Rather than scheduling three 'hours' a week, schedule in just three appointments with yourself. This could be an hour's workout, or it could be five minutes. Now what does a five-minute workout look like? Well, it could just be a stretch. It could be a walk in the park, it could be a few kettlebell swings, it could be five minutes of burpees. (Five minutes of burpees would suck.)

When the plan is realistic you are teeing up long-term consistency and therefore long-term success. Psychologically, you're **staying on the ball**.

This doesn't have to be just for your health and fitness. This same principle can be used in any area of your life.

The real secret is, if you schedule in three sessions and allow yourself to do five minutes, then as soon as you get started you will naturally do more than five minutes anyway.

Better yet...

plan around your vision.

Who you are, how you look and how you feel on a day-to-day basis. The details and the route you take to get there might change, but the vision stays consistent. This is your plan. And remember, regardless of what might get in your way, you **stick to the damn plan**.

15: Own or be owned

Oh, the irony! As it came time to write about this part of our philosophy, we procrastinated so much, not knowing where to start, or what would be the best format. Every section in this book is relatively short, we designed it that way, but this one in particular has taken three days to write. So far, 'Own or be owned' has... well... you know the rest.

The truth is, there may be different areas of your life that own you, and you just don't realise.

Maybe that car you bought, or that house, was a little too expensive – and now you're not living the life you want, due to the repayments you're responsible for.

Maybe you're mildly health conscious and buy packaged foods from the supermarket that say things like 'high in protein', 'low fat', 'source of fibre' or the hilarious 'good for you' range, but even so, still have excess body fat and don't feel amazing.

Maybe you struggle with time management or just can't fit everything into each day, yet still scroll through social media, watch TV or read newspapers. We are all owned from time to time without realising it, but when you have a plan for your life you must direct your energy and focus on owning what is important for you.

And when we say 'own', **we mean taking pride in every aspect of it; directing and shaping your life** so that every day your plan is pulled a little more into focus.

Focus
on creating your dream life,
or someone else will use you to create theirs.

Want to lose weight? Stop believing what you read on the labels of the foods you are buying. This is just marketing. It's designed to sell. Your health is not their first priority, your money is.

Own it!

Research what good nutrition looks like. This is not a weight-loss book, but here's a quick tip. If you

can go into nature and find it, gather it, forage for it, catch it or hunt it, then consider making it part of your diet. Fruit and vegetables of all kinds, nuts and seeds, pulses, legumes and meat (organic, free-range, ethically sourced) don't need a marketing team behind them. They have been the sources of nutrients for human beings since time began. But don't take our word for it either.

Own it!

Do your own research and make decisions for yourself about what you put into your body. Learn from multiple sources, then make an informed choice.

Want more financial freedom? Take a look at your income and outgoings. Are you being owned by what society says is normal? Spending any excess money you have on alcohol, entertainment, more clothes that you don't need, or upgrading your phone even though the phone you had was just fine? Are you owned by your job, working your socks off just to sustain a lifestyle that is designed by society rather than yourself?

Own it!

If you want to fill up a bathtub, before increasing the flow of water you must first put the plug in. Look at your spending habits and limit anything that doesn't add value to your life. Do you really want those things or are you just 'keeping up with the Joneses'? Are you just addicted to the release of hormones (dopamine, serotonin, adrenaline, endorphins) you get when you buy something new. What can you do to plug the outflow of money from your life?

Once you've stemmed the flow, you can look at your income. Start a business, develop one you already have, put steps in place so you can get a promotion, start a side-hustle. There's always something else you can do. Want to be happier? This is the big one. We wanted to give the examples of weight loss and financial freedom first, as these seem to be the most popular goals for most people. But when you break it all down, everything revolves around happiness.

Happiness = Reality minus Expectations

With the above equation in mind, ask yourself where your expectations are coming from. Have you been

owned by society, social media, mainstream media and maybe even by your own delusions about what it takes to feel good about yourself?

Own it!

Happiness can be found even on your darkest days. Understand your own mind and what you believe you NEED in any given moment. What you'll find is that you only need to breathe.

Everything else is just stuff. Stuff to make life more interesting, stuff to give you purpose, stuff to help you learn about yourself, stuff to entertain you, stuff to help you forget, stuff to help you remember.

This **meditative practice** can be done throughout your day. You don't have to light your incense and sit in the lotus position for this type of meditation. It's just simple observation.

We're all here to experience life.

The ups, the downs, the tos and the fros. Experience it all with an open heart but always remain centred. Just breathe and own your happiness.

16: The Viking mindset

The Viking Mindset was a video we produced for social media. It was short, scripted, cinematic and really enjoyable to make. Below you'll find the script from the video in bold with a longer explanation of each point below it.

A Viking never seeks hardship but is always ready for it.

However, in order to be ready for it, he MUST seek it out.

To experience true comfort is to first understand and embody discomfort.

The wisdom you gain from experience can never be faked, bought or cheated. You can read a million books on how to ride a bike but, in the end, you must put your big boy/girl pants on and risk falling off a few times if you are to stand a chance of riding anywhere.

This simple analogy applies to every area of your life.

You cannot have growth without struggle and hardship, so you should not only get used to being challenged but actively seek it out.

To be strong,

you must first find your weakness.

A chain is only ever as strong as its weakest link. A volleyball team can only ever be as good as their worst player. Likewise, you as an individual can only ever be as strong as your biggest weakness.

Don't be mistaken, amazing things happen when you build on your strengths, and we would always encourage you to do this. Unfortunately, we learn to hide weaknesses.

Much like any sports team, we believe subconsciously that if our weakness is highlighted, it can be exploited and taken advantage of. So, it's common to be defensive. To convince everyone (yourself included) that you're the finished product and that you're awesome.

Of course, you ARE awesome, but not in a finished product kind of way. You're awesome in the continuously self-improving, ever evolving, humble, honest and confident in your humility kind of way. If you seek out and work on your biggest weakness... you have no weakness.

It's only when you're willing to fail... that you're free to succeed.

As we've said before, growth comes out of struggle.

When your body or brain have been stressed, and then given time to adapt, you will come back stronger. This continuous cycle is what is known as success. Success is not a destination you arrive at.

But, of course, with stress and struggle failure might also come. Or at least what you perceive as failure. Failure and success are only opposites if you look at a situation in isolation. Failed a test. Missed a penalty kick. Didn't get that job. Gave up on your weight loss attempt.

The thing is... your life isn't a series of isolated events. It's a continuous, responsive and interwoven experience. Failure and success are not opposites. They are partners in the journey of growth. A 'failure' allows you to learn, learning leads to growth and that growth is what we call success.

To do this consistently, relentlessly and without wavering, you must have a vision for your life.

A vision so strong it lights a furnace in your belly and a fire in your heart.

An idea so inspiring that you're willing to move mountains, embrace adversity and do whatever it takes to make it a reality.

Ideas are good, but if you are not emotionally attached to them, they will soon be replaced by other ideas. To be clear, we're not talking about goal-setting here. Goal-setting is great, it allows you to be logical in your approach; what we're talking about here is your personal projection.

A projection isn't a goal that can either be achieved or not achieved. A projection is the path you are choosing to walk, and that path comes straight from your heart. Is your heart open?

Are you emotionally attached to your journey?

When you are faced with cold showers, gruelling workouts, new journeys putting strain on your relationships and that voice inside your head is asking, 'Why are you doing this?', do you have an answer for it?

Why stick to the damn plan when you can just relax, open a bottle of wine and watch a movie?
The answer to this question might be the only thing you will need to take from this book.

To be wise, you must accept your ignorance.

Even the greatest minds today are still trying to figure things out... how it all works and what we can do to advance humanity. It may seem like we know a lot and that we're doing a good job at expanding that knowledge, but seriously, as humans we've still got a long way to go. Yet there are still people who walk around thinking they know it all. It's hilarious, really.

We're sure you didn't need us to tell you that, but this is just a reminder to be childlike and inquisitive. Question everything and never stop learning. We only 'know' the past. If that's where you want to live, then you're reading the wrong book. If you're excited for your future and all its potentialities, then...

Live your life with a
Viking mindset.

17: Progression over perfection

Progression in every element of your life is vital to be successful at anything you do.

Perfection is an unattainable goal. Much like infinity, one can seek it but will never find it.

And yet so many people spend their time trying to create the perfect plan for themselves. They worry about where they're starting from, and will naturally compare themselves to friends, family and social media icons.

Perhaps Hollywood needs to shoulder some of the blame here, in terms of their awe-inspiring films packed with epic training montages that increase gym membership sales every time they are released.

You know the kind of movies? The type that make you want to go for a run as soon as you've finished watching. You slap the soundtrack onto your playlist and you relive the energy the main character had when smashing through their gruelling training regime to achieve their goals.

If your favourite character can do it, why can't you?

Because it's fiction. Because the main character in the movie didn't have to adjust their training day to look after a sick child. Because that same character's fridge never ran out of eggs and chicken. They never caught a cold, got stuck in traffic or were hindered by any of the real life stuff that gets in our way when we are trying to better ourselves.

As far as the movie would have you believe, that character got down to some hard 'blood, sweat and tears' training and got the job done!

Naturally, we try to mimic this, setting unreasonable training plans with unattainable goals. It feels good for the first few days because it's tough. That's what you wanted, right? You're living that movie. Until stress and fatigue kicks in and you miss a session. **You did WHAT?** That didn't happen in the movie. Now you feel unworthy in your own journey, like you wouldn't be cast in your own life story!

You miss another session, you eat something that is off-plan and before you know it you've fallen

completely off the wagon. You rest for a few days, still eating off-plan. Energy levels come back up, you feel better, you think to yourself, 'It was just a blip, I'll start fresh again this coming Monday.'

But it's only Thursday.

So you fall prey to **'last supper syndrome'**, consuming all the foods you know won't be available from next week onwards. You pile on some more weight and feel sluggish but it's okay, you'll sort it come Monday.

Monday comes and you start again. And, sure enough, by Wednesday you've quit.

It's this approach that has given the fitness industry a level of mystique for those that don't participate in it. They can't see past the perfect approach and therefore it's all or nothing. This is simply not the case.

Everyone is different and develops at a different pace.

The only thing that matters is that you establish where you are right now, and that you make progress over the coming weeks, months and years.

Progress is key.

You'll ask yourself, well, what is progress? If it's exercise, it might mean one extra rep or a little more weight. It might mean going to the gym for an extra session that week or spending ten minutes longer doing cardio.

That is progress.

When it comes to lifestyle factors you might think, 'I don't have time to exercise.'

Set your alarm two minutes earlier.

Two minutes? 'That isn't going to solve anything,' you might say.

It's a start. It's progress.

Once you get used to waking up two minutes earlier, you can go for a slightly longer shower, you can make some breakfast. Then aim to wake up five minutes earlier, then ten minutes, then double that.

Slowly but surely, you're creating a lifestyle that makes your goal possible to achieve.

You can then **look to your hydration levels**.

Check if you're drinking enough water each day. And if you struggle to hit a particular water target initially, aim for 200 millilitres more than you were drinking before and build up.

Once you complete one full day of this, **go for a streak**. Multiple days on the trot. If in one week you get two days back-to-back with success, the following week go for three days back-to-back. That's progress.

Have a look at all the areas in your life where you want to make improvements, then measure where are you right now.

Look at where you want to be and look at the first natural step.

Keep making little bits of progress, regardless of how big or small those progressions are.

Just make progress and you'll be sticking to the damn plan!

18: That one thing to guarantee success

We all experience times when we feel run off our feet. This can be due to work, family commitments or maybe an event that you're helping to organise that's grabbing all of your attention.

You might have told friends you can't meet them because you're super busy or you've got so much on your plate. Having so much to do can feel overwhelming and, speaking from experience, it can cause anxiety.

You find yourself stressed out, almost paralysed by the weight of tasks bearing down on you. You feel down and like you're not sticking to the damn plan.

In situations like that, it's important to analyse the tasks that you do have to get done that day. Do this first thing in the morning. Just take a moment and

breathe – you don't want this analysis to overwhelm you.

Think of it as a stock-take. Grab a pen and paper and make sure you **write down ONLY tasks that need done that day**. You can add approximate times to each if you wish, but the goal here is to establish exactly how your day is going to look. One thing's for sure, not all 'busy' days are created equal.

The next task is to prioritise the tasks on the list.

Establish **what absolutely needs completed** and what is secondary.

In other words, which tasks will cause the world to end if they are not done and which will not?

As coaches, we would argue that nothing will cause the world to end, but let's just play along for now.

Now you have your list of primaries and secondaries. If you can get the primaries completed it's a successful day, and any secondaries are bonuses.

The next job is adding in a little **'stick to the damn plan'**. (You thought you'd got away with that, didn't you?)

We always need to make time for our health and fitness, no matter how busy we are, but redefining what that means during a busy period is what we like to call 'that one thing to guarantee success'.

So looking at your list ask yourself, 'What **DO** I have time for today that would further my health and fitness?'

Pick one thing – just one thing – that, when achieved, counts as a health success.

This can be something as simple as going for a five-minute walk to fill your lungs with fresh air and get some energy flowing through your body.

It could be something as simple as having breakfast, drinking plenty of water or avoiding starchy carbs.

It could be getting your food prep done at the start at the day to save you having to worry about meals later. If you've got your food prep done, you're going to eat properly. You might not have time to train or to get other things done, but that one thing is in the bag.

Now, depending on how busy you are, the one thing you have chosen to complete today can become

bigger if you've got less to do overall and vice versa: the less time you have, the smaller that 'one thing' becomes. However, when you achieve that one thing, you will still feel fantastic. You will get a dopamine release in the brain (the success hormone, if you like) and you will feel accomplished.

And this is how we stick to the damn plan, even when we're busy.

Win each day.

Win your life.

A note about our kilts & logo

Our kilts.
Our superhero costume.
Our armour.
Our identity.

From the moment we first put on the kilts we felt drawn to a version of ourselves that felt free. Free from the shackles of the expectations of others, free from restraints, we were able to **completely be ourselves** (much like we described in Chapter 1: 'Be yourself in HD').

What we commonly get asked about is, why that particular tartan? Well firstly, we chose the **Royal Stewart** as it is one of the most widely recognisable tartans out there plus its main colours are red and yellow. Since our own family tartans wouldn't allow for much of a uniform approach, we chose the Royal Stewart to give our videos a solid and visible identity.

We have since then created **our own 'The Kilted Coaches' tartan**, which pays homage to our original plaid while leaning towards a slightly deeper red. In all honesty, this was mostly down to the socks we like to wear being a maroon colour which we preferred to the striking red of Royal Stewart.

One thing that has remained a constant along the way is our red and yellow latticed logo (shown above), which is also represented within the weave of the tartan itself. Our logo is symbolic of the synergy between our two personalities. Kind of like the **Yin and Yang**, although with a bit of colour. We are two very different people and when we come together, a certain creative magic happens that has birthed many projects – one of these being the book you hold in your hands right now.

People often asked whether there was also a deeper symbolism in the particular colours we chose for our logo. We actually created a video about this in the early days and we explained how we delved deeply into the realms of colour charts and **hidden meaning** to create something we were proud to wear on our chests, display on our website and now talk about in our book.

Red and the yellow, both primary colours, have many meanings, particularly when used in movies. But here we'll touch on the elements that are important to any **wellness improvement journey**.

Red signifies strength, determination, passion and motivation.
If you are embarking on a fitness program, you will need all of these to get the engine **fired up** and ready to go. **Red signifies the body of work,** the vessel upon which your journey will embark upon.

Yellow signifies hope, happiness, clarity and optimism, all vital if any goal is to have direction – a pilot at the helm, if you like, someone to steer you on the way and keep you on the right track.

Combined in a lattice formation, they suggest an **unstoppable union** that is fired up for the journey and focused on the destination. As you can see from the logo, neither side higher or lower, or of more or less importance. It represents **balanced partnership**.

Ultimately, if you want more health, happiness and success in your life, then this logo symbolises the power you already have within to make anything you desire **manifest in reality**.

Luath Press Limited

committed to publishing well written books worth reading

LUATH PRESS takes its name from Robert Burns, whose little collie Luath (*Gael.*, swift or nimble) tripped up Jean Armour at a wedding and gave him the chance to speak to the woman who was to be his wife and the abiding love of his life. Burns called one of the 'Twa Dogs' Luath after Cuchullin's hunting dog in Ossian's *Fingal*. Luath Press was established in 1981 in the heart of Burns country, and is now based a few steps up the road from Burns' first lodgings on Edinburgh's Royal Mile. Luath offers you distinctive writing with a hint of unexpected pleasures.

Most bookshops in the UK, the US, Canada, Australia, New Zealand and parts of Europe, either carry our books in stock or can order them for you. To order direct from us, please send a £sterling cheque, postal order, international money order or your credit card details (number, address of cardholder and expiry date) to us at the address below. Please add post and packing as follows: UK – £1.00 per delivery address; overseas surface mail – £2.50 per delivery address; overseas airmail – £3.50 for the first book to each delivery address, plus £1.00 for each additional book by airmail to the same address. If your order is a gift, we will happily enclose your card or message at no extra charge.

Luath Press Limited
543/2 Castlehill
The Royal Mile
Edinburgh EH1 2ND
Scotland
Telephone: +44 (0)131 225 4326 (24 hours)
Email: sales@luath.co.uk
Website: www.luath.co.uk